# Phonic

Building
Reading
Success

### Consultant

Sandra J. Fehr, Ph.D.

### Publisher's Project Staff

| | |
|---|---|
| Vice President, Product Development: | Kathleen T. Williams, Ph.D., NCSP |
| Managing Editor: | Blanche Bolland |
| Designer: | Tony Perleberg |
| Desktop Publishing Specialist 2: | Linda Peterson |
| Design Manager: | Nancy Condon |
| Materials Planner/Buyer 2: | Martha Erding |
| Associate Marketing Director: | Maureen O'Brien |

©2002 AGS Publishing
4201 Woodland Road, Circle Pines, MN 55014-1796
(800)328-2560   www.agsnet.com

AGS Publishing is a trademark of American Guidance Service, Inc.

Product Number: 91816        A 0 9 8 7 6 5 4 3 2

# Where's the Accent? 1

**Directions**   If the accent is on the first syllable, put a check mark in front of the word. If the accent is on the second syllable, put a check mark after the word.

| | | |
|---|---|---|
| able | finish | police |
| above | follow | question |
| asleep | haven't | return |
| because | himself | someone |
| biggest | inside | suppose |
| cannot | kitchen | taken |
| donkey | machine | today |
| enough | maybe | until |
| even | o'clock | useful |
| excite | office | village |

# Where's the Accent? 2

**Directions**   If the accent is on the first syllable, put a check mark in front of the word. If the accent is on the second syllable, put a check mark after the word.

| | | |
|---|---|---|
| aboard | cabin | enjoy |
| airport | canoe | except |
| alarm | careless | extra |
| announce | complain | foolish |
| arrow | complete | forgive |
| baggage | correct | fortune |
| became | courage | garage |
| begun | darkness | harbor |
| blossom | delight | highway |
| borrow | doesn't | indeed |

# Where's the Accent? 3

**Directions** If the accent is on the first syllable, put a check mark in front of the word. If the accent is on the second syllable, put a check mark after the word.

| | | |
|---|---|---|
| insect | ocean | themselves |
| invite | outdoors | Thursday |
| itself | pencil | toward |
| July | perhaps | tower |
| lazy | polite | unite |
| manage | pretend | unless |
| mayor | promise | valley |
| metal | receive | welcome |
| mistake | reply | women |
| nation | sandwich | zero |

# L or R?

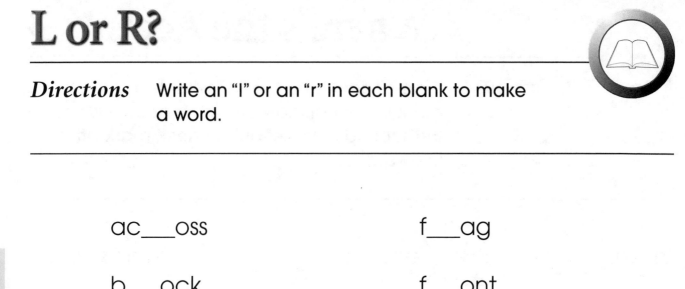

**Directions**   Write an "l" or an "r" in each blank to make a word.

ac___oss            f___ag

b___ock             f___ont

b___ave             g___ove

b___oken            g___ay

c___ean             g___ew

c___imb             g___in

c___ose             p___ace

c___eam             p___ant

c___awl             p___int

d___ive             s___ed

**Directions**    Write the initial blend to complete the word shown in the picture across from it.

| pr | tr | gr | br | cr | dr |

_____ess

_____ain  _____ack

_____ush

_____um

_____ice

_____apes

_____esident

_____own

_____uck

# Start Me Up! 2

**Directions**    Write the initial blend to complete each word shown in the picture across from it.

| cl | gl | sc | sk | sp | st |

\_\_\_\_\_oud

\_\_\_\_\_oves

\_\_\_\_\_unk

\_\_\_\_\_asses

\_\_\_\_\_ider

\_\_\_\_\_othing

\_\_\_\_\_oon

\_\_\_\_\_ar

\_\_\_\_\_ale

**Directions**     Write the final blend to complete each word
shown in the picture across from it.

Consonants
Blends

| nt | st | nk | nd |

ba_____

pla_____

li_____

diamo_____

te_____

pa_____e

tru_____

toa_____

sku_____

# Finish Us Off 2

**Directions**   Write the final blend to complete each word shown in the picture across from it.

| ft | mp | rt | rd | lf |
|----|----|----|----|----|

repo_____ ca_____

sta_____

bea_____

hea_____

ca_____

gi_____

ha_____

shi_____

la_____

Consonants
Blends

# Put Me in My Place

**Directions**   Write the digraph from a circle in each blank to make a word.

**ch**     **sh**     **th**     **wh**

_____ought                _____icken

_____air                  _____imney

_____ale                  _____ort

_____all                  _____ile

_____ovel                 _____row

_____ange                 _____isper

_____rew                  _____eir

_____ase                  _____ould

_____eel                  _____out

_____ook                  _____em

_____rough                _____ipmunk

_____ich                  _____o

9

*Phonic*

# Do I Sound Hard?

**Directions**     Underline the "c"s that sound hard like in "block."

Consonants

Hard & Soft

across

because

bicycle

cage

candle

cent

chance

change

chicken

circus

city

clean

cook

crawl

cutting

excite

face

fence

ice cream

lock

machine

magic

neck

o'clock

office

picnic

piece

place

police

popcorn

princess

raccoon

race

school

second

secret

ticket

tractor

voice

# Do I Sound Soft?

**Directions**  Underline the "g"s that sound soft like in "age."

| | | |
|---|---|---|
| ago | flag | orange |
| beginning | gate | rag |
| biggest | glove | riding |
| bridge | grandmother | ring |
| building | | song |
| cage | | strange |
| change | | string |
| dig | hungry | tag |
| edge | large | together |
| engine | magic | village |
| evening | making | wag |

# What Am I?

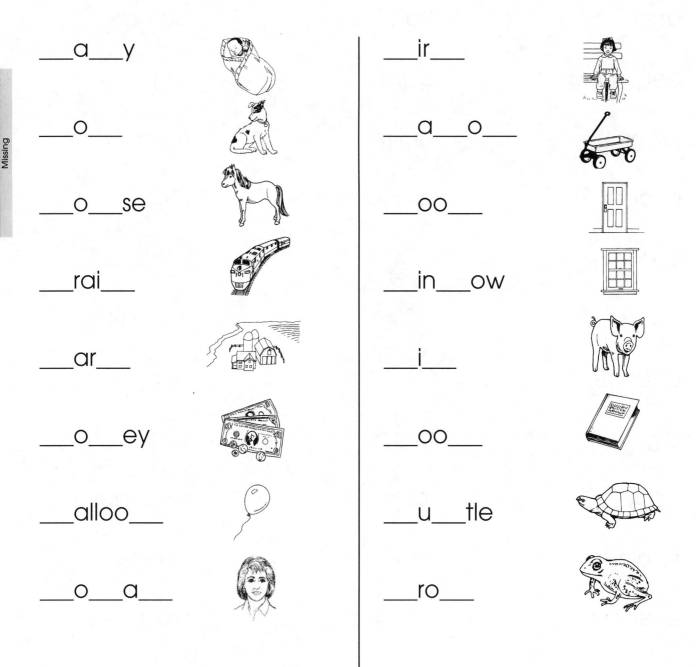

**Directions**    Fill in the missing letters in these words that match the pictures across from them.

__a__y

__o__

__o__se

__rai__

__ar__

__o__ey

__alloo__

__o__a__

__ir__

__a__o__

__oo__

__in__ow

__i__

__oo__

__u__tle

__ro__

# Flyaway Letters *1*

**Directions**    Fill in the missing letter in each word. Use one of the four letters in the balloons.

cal___                bir___

**b**

a___out            alo___g

**d**

lam___              ___ever

___arm             a___y

**f**

gar___en           ba___y

___oll               be___ore

**n**

# Flyaway Letters 2

**Directions**    Fill in the missing letter in each word. Use one of the three letters in the balloons.

b___             part___

**o**

p___ll           ab___ut

___ver          ___ard

**u**

g___ne          stor___

___ncle         w___rd

**y**

r___nning       h___rry

# Flyaway Letters 3

**Directions**  Fill in the missing letter in each word. Use one of the three letters in the balloons.

hon___y                    ___sked

cook___e                   flow___r

br___ng                    bo___t

___gg                      morn___ng

c___ke                     ___nto

fri___nd                   ___unt

a

e

i

# Flyaway Letters *4*

ever___          ___agon

stor___          ___heir

fo___            ___es

wen___           clo___n

da___            ne___t

be___ter         windo___

t

w

x

y

# Flyaway Letters 5

**Directions**   Fill in the missing letter in each word. Use one of the four letters in the balloons.

ste___                    tho___e

wi___h                    ___ark

sto___y                   ___ery

s___ring                  ___hoe

gi___e                    ___ead

we___e                    hel___

**p**

**r**

**s**

**v**

Consonants

Missing

17

*Phonic*

# Flyaway Letters 6

**Directions**   Fill in the missing letter in each word. Use one of the four letters in the balloons.

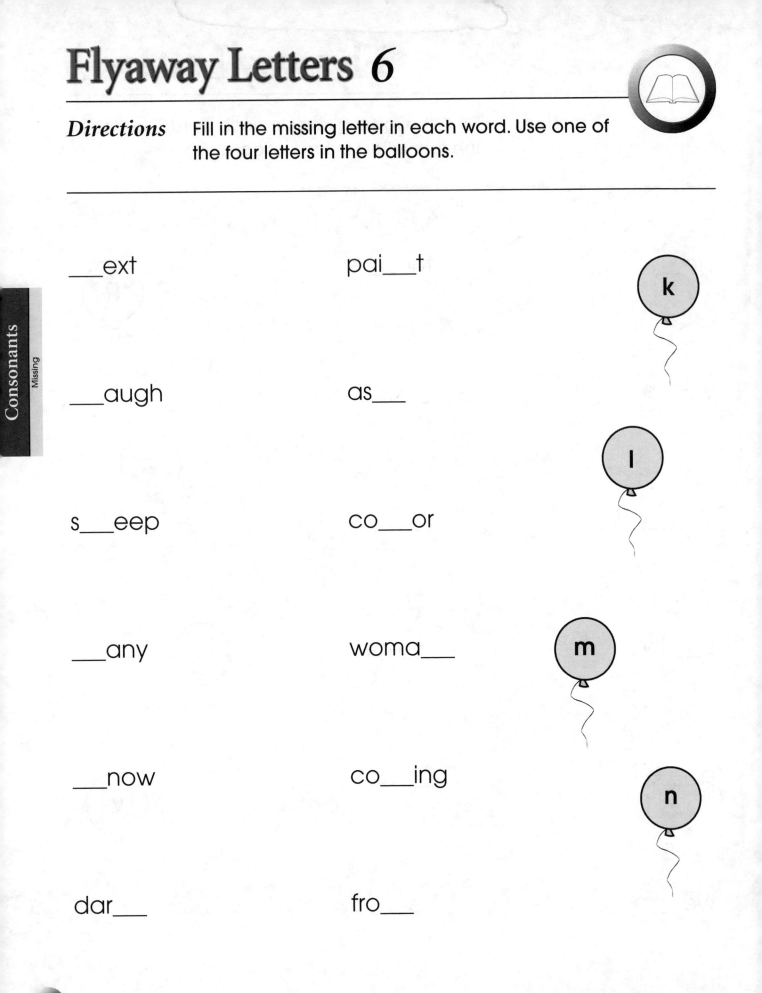

__ext                        pai__t

__augh                       as__

s__eep                       co__or

__any                        woma__

__now                        co__ing

dar__                        fro__

k

l

m

n

# Flyaway Letters 7

___irl                on___e

___uess               be___ind

___lown               s___hool

alon___               ___appy

ba___k                ___ust

a___ain               eac___

**c**

**g**

**h**

**j**

# Runaway Letters *1*

**Directions**  Find the runaway letter to complete each word.

__ouch

__est

dri__e

__ntil

co__y

__ero

__orn

exi__

an__

b__rn

be__ond

jo__

ali__e

la__y

ha__k

eno__gh

wo__nd

e__ent

grea__

kne__

o__e

pri__e

__isit

stud__

# Runaway Letters *2*

**Directions**    Find the runaway letter to complete each word.

ai___                     wor___t

___igh                    stac___

___ale                    ___tare

___noc___                 lea___

___oin                    ca___m

___abe___                 ___ur___le

ob___ect                  en___oy

wrin___le                 pau___e

___arch                   co___ ___on

woo___                    o___en

___ewel                   bar___

stu___p                   s___ope

Letters

Missing

21

*Phonic*

# Runaway Letters *3*

**Directions**     Find the runaway letter to complete each word.

| | |
|---|---|
| c__l__r | Mon___ay |
| fa___ | sti___ |
| wa___n | si___ewalk |
| bo___y | p___ice |
| fe___ | sa___d |
| b___g | b___at |
| a___t | ___hi___k |
| w___ak | b___y |
| i___e | ___aise |
| ___gg | ___orth |
| poli___e | mil___ |
| be___ame | d___sk |

Letters

Missing

# Runaway Letters 4

**Directions**    Find the runaway letter to complete each word.

a__le

d__v__de

__ait

dan__er

__im

bunc__

a__e

a__ __ord

cur__ous

c__ain

e__ghty

gi__nt

rus__

__bo__rd

co__we__

ha__it

__naw

__alse

ne__t

fla__

__ire

l__e

sel__

wr__p

Letters

Missing

# I Can't Hear You! 1

**Directions**   Cross out the letters that you can't hear.

again          head          rain

alone          high          ready

aunt           ice cream     show

boat           know          walk

cake           lamb          were

calf           light         window

each           paint

five           peanut

guess          people

afraid        climb        knock

ahead        could        leaves

answer        crow        oak

beautiful        edge        reach

board        feather        sign

bought        flashlight        straight

bread        fruit        suit

bridge        great        tonight

# I Can't Hear You! 3

**Directions**    Cross out the letters that you can't hear.

aim

autumn

blueberry

built

chief

continue

curious

daughter

dumb

famous

guide

highway

honor

hose

hour

island

judge

juice

knife

lie

lonely

match

tight

wrap

# I Can't Hear You! 4

| | | |
|---|---|---|
| borrow | patch | sigh |
| gnaw | piano | somebody |
| guard | pitcher | taught |
| known | receive | themselves |
| lovely | rescue | weren't |
| meadow | safety | wheat |
| ninety | scratch | whole |
| often | serious | wouldn't |

Silent Letters

# Color the Rhyme *1*

Color the word that rhymes with <u>could</u> blue.

Color the word that rhymes with <u>all</u> white.

Color the word that rhymes with <u>many</u> green.

Color the word that rhymes with <u>she</u> brown.

Color the word that rhymes with <u>are</u> red.

Color the word that rhymes with <u>how</u> black.

Color the word that rhymes with <u>honey</u> yellow.

Color the word that rhymes with <u>made</u> orange.

| any | car | money | ball |
|-----|-----|-------|------|
| bee | would | stayed | cow |

# Color the Rhyme 2

**Directions**    Look for the underlined word in each sentence. Then color the box with the word that rhymes with it.

Color the word that rhymes with <u>name</u> white.

Color the word that rhymes with <u>be</u> red.

Color the word that rhymes with <u>too</u> brown.

Color the word that rhymes with <u>found</u> yellow.

Color the word that rhymes with <u>sing</u> blue.

Color the word that rhymes with <u>ice</u> black.

Color the word that rhymes with <u>hat</u> green.

Color the word that rhymes with <u>long</u> orange.

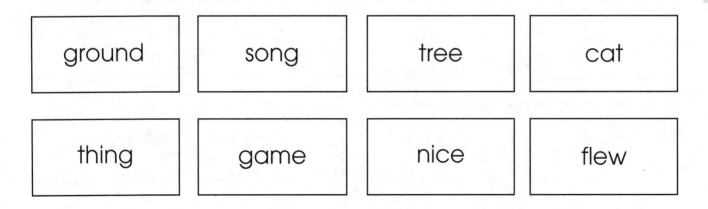

| | | | |
|---|---|---|---|
| ground | song | tree | cat |
| thing | game | nice | flew |

# Color the Rhyme 3

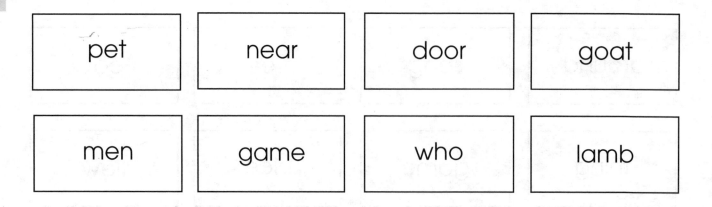

Color the word that rhymes with <u>came</u> red.

Color the word that rhymes with <u>wet</u> yellow.

Color the word that rhymes with <u>am</u> black.

Color the word that rhymes with <u>more</u> green.

Color the word that rhymes with <u>when</u> white.

Color the word that rhymes with <u>new</u> brown.

Color the word that rhymes with <u>here</u> blue.

Color the word that rhymes with <u>boat</u> orange.

| pet | near | door | goat |
|-----|------|------|------|
| men | game | who | lamb |

Rhyming

# Two Who Do Rhyme 1

**Directions**    Next to each word below, print a word from the box that rhymes with it.

cat _____          frog _____

bed _____          tree _____

bone _____         mouse _____

goat _____         rug _____

deer _____         cry _____

mail _____         snow _____

Rhyming

| key | bug | cone | sled | fear | dog |
|-----|-----|------|------|------|-----|
| sky | blow | coat | nail | hat | house |

# Two Who Do Rhyme 2

**Directions**  Next to each word below, print a word from the box that rhymes with it.

book _____          fly _____

mail _____          paw _____

soap _____          dish _____

lip _____           rock _____

jump _____          bun _____

rain _____          mice _____

| ship | claw | slice | pail | fry | pump |
|------|------|-------|------|-----|------|
| fish | lock | pain | hope | look | fun |

# Change My Vowel 1

**Directions**   Change the vowel in each word to make a new word. Print the word on the blank by the old word.

fur _____    want _____    list _____

bug _____    come _____    man _____

give _____    bay _____    wish _____

now _____    same _____    bat _____

an _____    barn _____    block _____

# Change My Vowel *2*

***Directions***   Change the vowel in each word to make a
new word. Print the word on the blank by the
old word.

ham _____   deck _____   fist _____

hot _____   knew _____   think _____

son _____   most _____   fit _____

run _____   sew _____   pill _____

but _____   cut _____   dig _____

Vowels   Changes

**Directions**   Change the vowel in each word to make a new word. Print the word on the blank by the old word.

song _____     tall _____     love _____

get _____     those _____     bell _____

sit _____     us _____     than _____

bed _____     stop _____     ill _____

his _____     lot _____     of _____

# Long or Short "a"?

**Directions**     Write the words from the box where they belong.

| | | |
|---|---|---|
| ask | fast | paint |
| back | gave | rain |
| cake | lamb | stay |
| cat | name | than |

**Short "a" sound**

**Long "a" sound**

# Long or Short "e"?

| be | egg | please |
|----|-----|--------|
| bed | feet | sleep |
| dress | hen | tell |
| eat | pet | went |

## Long "e" sound

## Short "e" sound

# Long or Short "i"?

**Directions**     Write the words from the box where
they belong.

| fine | his | prize |
|------|-----|-------|
| fish | ice | right |
| give | if | sit |
| hill | pig | try |

| Long "i" sound | Short "i" sound |
|----------------|-----------------|
| ● | ● |
| | |
| | |
| | |
| ● | ● |
| | |
| | |
| ● | ● |
| | |

# Long or Short "o"?

**Directions**   Write the words from the box where they belong.

| | | |
|---|---|---|
| boat | doll | nose |
| box | grow | off |
| cold | hot | road |
| dog | lost | so |

## Long "o" sound

- 

## Short "o" sound

- 

Vowels

Long & Short

# Long or Short "u"?

**Directions**   Write the words from the box where they belong.

| | | |
|---|---|---|
| blue | huge | sun |
| but | just | truck |
| cup | lunch | true |
| duck | much | use |

## Long "u" sound

- 
- 
- 

## Short "u" sound

- 
- 
-

# Am I Long?

| | | |
|---|---|---|
| all | fire | keep |
| baby | first | kept |
| be | foot | kind |
| bed | frog | king |
| bird | glad | lad |
| book | goat | love |
| but | goose | low |
| by | gray | might |
| cake | grow | no |
| calf | hand | owl |
| can't | hill | own |
| coat | hold | pie |
| day | hot | right |
| don't | if | roll |
| feet | I'll | sell |
| find | isn't | sleep |

# Am I Short?

**Directions**    Underline all the words that have a **short** vowel sound.

| | | |
|---|---|---|
| aim | from | smell |
| ask | give | smile |
| ax | grass | snow |
| bag | hay | spring |
| best | hen | street |
| black | I'm | tiny |
| bus | it's | tried |
| catch | knock | us |
| cold | most | use |
| cry | mud | way |
| dog | oh | weigh |
| dress | only | well |
| each | she | we'll |
| egg | shiny | wild |
| fine | sign | wind |
| fish | sky | won't |

**Vowels**
Long & Short

42

Phonic

**Directions**    Write the words from the box where they belong.

| | | | | |
|---|---|---|---|---|
| act | case | inn | nine | save |
| add | cup | job | note | tube |
| age | dip | led | page | won |
| base | elf | mile | pin | yet |
| beg | hose | net | rose | |

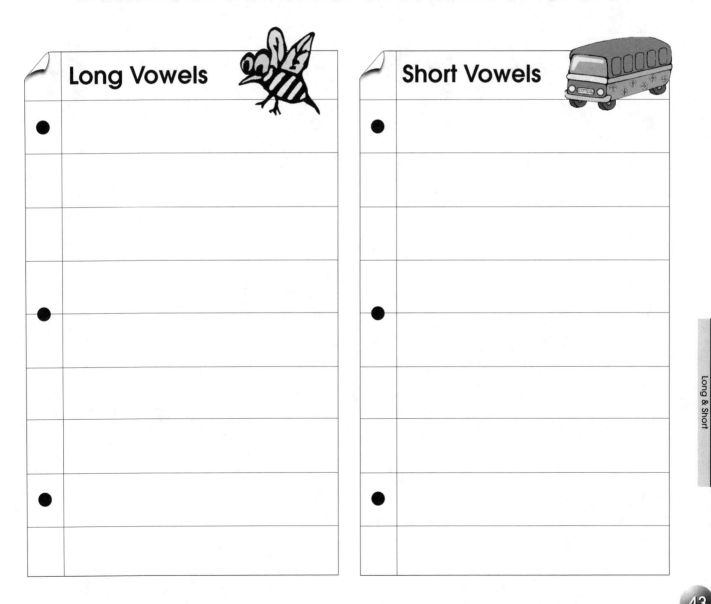

### Long Vowels

### Short Vowels

# Long or Short? 2

**Directions**   Write the words from the box where they belong.

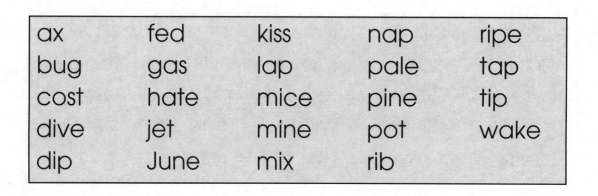

| ax   | fed  | kiss | nap  | ripe |
| bug  | gas  | lap  | pale | tap  |
| cost | hate | mice | pine | tip  |
| dive | jet  | mine | pot  | wake |
| dip  | June | mix  | rib  |      |

| **Long Vowels** | **Short Vowels** |
|---|---|
| ● | ● |
| | |
| | |
| | |
| ● | ● |
| | |
| | |
| ● | ● |
| | |

# Long or Short? 3

***Directions***   Write the words from the box where they belong.

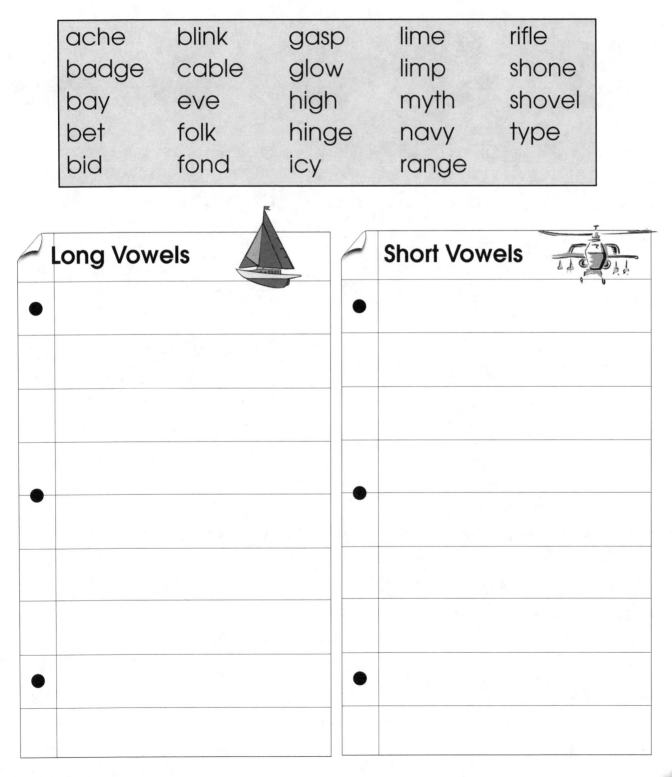

| | | | | |
|---|---|---|---|---|
| ache | blink | gasp | lime | rifle |
| badge | cable | glow | limp | shone |
| bay | eve | high | myth | shovel |
| bet | folk | hinge | navy | type |
| bid | fond | icy | range | |

## Long Vowels

## Short Vowels

Vowels

Long & Short

# Pick a Vowel *1*

**Directions**    In each blank, write a vowel from one of the flowers to make a word.

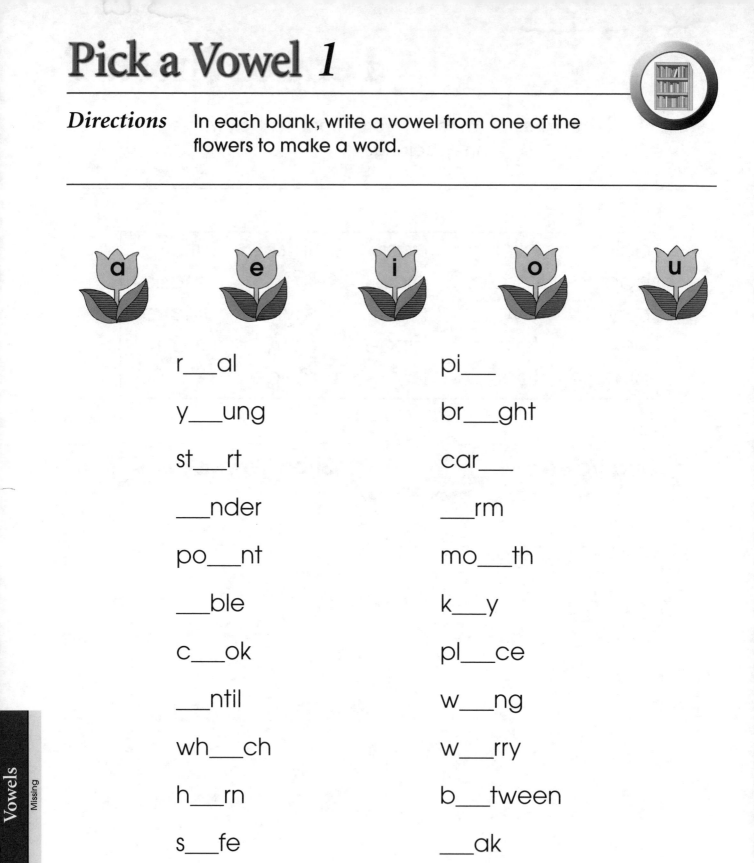

a    e    i    o    u

r___al              pi___

y___ung             br___ght

st___rt             car___

___nder             ___rm

po___nt             mo___th

___ble              k___y

c___ok              pl___ce

___ntil             w___ng

wh___ch             w___rry

h___rn              b___tween

s___fe              ___ak

co___nt             c___ty

# Pick a Vowel 2

**Directions**  In each blank, write a vowel from one of the flowers to make a word.

a    e    i    o    u

bu___ld          tr___nk

de___p           eno___gh

gl___ve          n___il

___ir            ___nhappy

e___rly          k___nd

b___te           ma___l

w___'ll          l___te

yo___r           m___ve

___ts            ___nly

___se            b___rk

g___es           th___ught

r___st           li___n

# Pick a Vowel 3

**Directions**   Write the missing vowel in each blank.

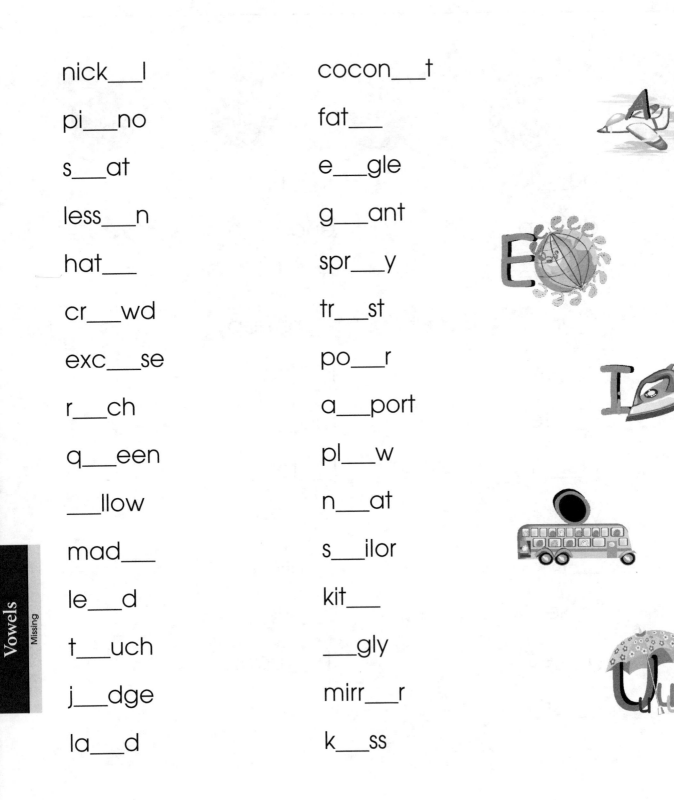

nick__l

pi__no

s__at

less__n

hat__

cr__wd

exc__se

r__ch

q__een

__llow

mad__

le__d

t__uch

j__dge

la__d

cocon__t

fat__

e__gle

g__ant

spr__y

tr__st

po__r

a__port

pl__w

n__at

s__ilor

kit__

__gly

mirr__r

k__ss

# Pick a Vowel 4

**Directions**   Write the missing vowel in each blank.

fe___st

her___

s___dden

m___rch

at___

compla___n

po___nd

tap___

c___ach

Sp___in

g___ard

___ften

d___p

___ron

din___

cut___

flo___t

e___ghty

als___

ch___ckle

___pon

shad___w

d___scover

re___r

dim___

s___ld

h___ge

esc___pe

o___l

rat___

A

E

I

O

U

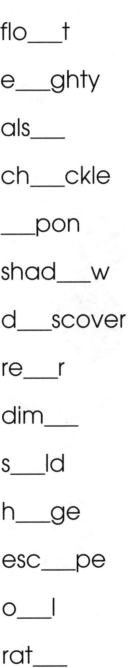

Vowels

Missing

# Ouch!

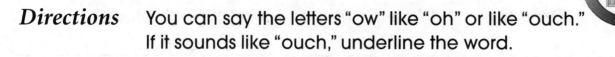

**Directions**    You can say the letters "ow" like "oh" or like "ouch."
If it sounds like "ouch," underline the word.

allow                                          low

arrow                                          narrow

blow                                           now

brown                                          owl

clown                                          own

cow                                            show

drown                                          snow

flower                                         throw

grow                                           town

growl                                          window

how                                            wow

know                                           yellow

# Structural

Building
Reading
Success

# 1, 2, 3... A, B, C... 1

**Directions**     On the numbered lines, write the countries from the box in alphabetical order.

| | | | |
|---|---|---|---|
| Kenya | Russia | Spain | Egypt |
| Peru | Cuba | New Zealand | India |
| France | Laos | Japan | Greece |

1. _____

2. _____

3. _____

4. _____

5. _____

6. _____

7. _____

8. _____

9. _____

10. _____

11. _____

12. _____

| | | | |
|---|---|---|---|
| Sudan | Brazil | Zaire | Poland |
| Israel | Norway | Australia | China |
| Germany | Korea | Thailand | Mexico |

1. _____

2. _____

3. _____

4. _____

5. _____

6. _____

7. _____

8. _____

9. _____

10. _____

11. _____

12. _____

# 1, 2, 3... A, B, C... 2

**Directions**    On the numbered lines, write the names from the box in alphabetical order.

| | | | |
|---|---|---|---|
| Isabelle | Eduardo | Phan | Michael |
| Brooke | Madeline | Jennifer | Jacob |
| Paige | Andrew | Hailey | Aaron |

1. _____
2. _____
3. _____
4. _____
5. _____
6. _____

7. _____
8. _____
9. _____
10. _____
11. _____
12. _____

| | | | |
|---|---|---|---|
| Tyrell | Zachary | Daniel | Caitlin |
| Nicholas | Sarah | Tamiko | Zoe |
| Kate | Justin | Christopher | Melanie |

1. _____
2. _____
3. _____
4. _____
5. _____
6. _____

7. _____
8. _____
9. _____
10. _____
11. _____
12. _____

# 1, 2, 3... A, B, C... 3

**Directions**  On the numbered lines, write the names from the box in alphabetical order.

| | | | |
|---|---|---|---|
| Nathaniel | Micah | Lindsay | Cameron |
| Robert | Chloe | Rachel | Luke |
| Laura | Matthew | Noah | Nicole |

1. _____
2. _____
3. _____
4. _____
5. _____
6. _____

7. _____
8. _____
9. _____
10. _____
11. _____
12. _____

| | | | |
|---|---|---|---|
| Sawyer | Talebi | Sharif | Ly |
| Kaminsky | Sonderman | Khan | Dahl |
| Delano | Levine | Thoma | LaSalle |

1. _____
2. _____
3. _____
4. _____
5. _____
6. _____

7. _____
8. _____
9. _____
10. _____
11. _____
12. _____

# Order Us Around 1

**Directions**  On the numbered lines, write the names
from the box in alphabetical order.

| | | | |
|---|---|---|---|
| Montreal | Rome | London | Oslo |
| Dublin | Vienna | Baghdad | Zurich |
| Tokyo | New York | Athens | Paris |
| Houston | Sydney | Winnipeg | Chicago |

1. _____
2. _____
3. _____
4. _____
5. _____
6. _____
7. _____
8. _____

9. _____
10. _____
11. _____
12. _____
13. _____
14. _____
15. _____
16. _____

| | | | |
|---|---|---|---|
| Ohio | Rhode Island | Maine | Virginia |
| Florida | Nevada | Delaware | Texas |
| Wyoming | Hawaii | Georgia | Iowa |
| Kansas | Arizona | Colorado | Utah |

1. _____
2. _____
3. _____
4. _____
5. _____
6. _____
7. _____
8. _____

9. _____
10. _____
11. _____
12. _____
13. _____
14. _____
15. _____
16. _____

# Order Us Around 2

**Directions**  On the numbered lines, write the names from the box in alphabetical order.

| | | | |
|---|---|---|---|
| Taylor | SooLee | Trevor | Stephanie |
| Seth | Sean | Sierra | Saied |
| Sasha | Tao | Tyeisha | Tyrone |
| Thomas | Shannon | Samuel | Shelby |

1. _____
2. _____
3. _____
4. _____
5. _____
6. _____
7. _____
8. _____

9. _____
10. _____
11. _____
12. _____
13. _____
14. _____
15. _____
16. _____

| | | | |
|---|---|---|---|
| Bryce | Abigail | Allison | Bailey |
| Angelina | Brandon | Adam | Arianne |
| Benjamin | Alexander | Blake | Andrea |
| Amanda | Brianna | Alicia | Bik |

1. _____
2. _____
3. _____
4. _____
5. _____
6. _____
7. _____
8. _____

9. _____
10. _____
11. _____
12. _____
13. _____
14. _____
15. _____
16. _____

# Order Us Around 3

**Directions**   On the numbered lines, write the names from the box in alphabetical order.

| | | | |
|---|---|---|---|
| Eric | Holden | Emily | Dante |
| Destiny | Dakota | Devin | Ethan |
| David | Elizabeth | Gabriella | Grace |
| Emma | Dominique | Evan | Dylan |

1. _____
2. _____
3. _____
4. _____
5. _____
6. _____
7. _____
8. _____

9. _____
10. _____
11. _____
12. _____
13. _____
14. _____
15. _____
16. _____

| | | | |
|---|---|---|---|
| Kyle | Kristen | Jordan | Jasmine |
| Javier | Jenaya | Kayla | Keiko |
| Kevin | Jamal | Jackson | Jesse |
| Julianna | Joshua | Kareem | Jonathan |

1. _____
2. _____
3. _____
4. _____
5. _____
6. _____
7. _____
8. _____

9. _____
10. _____
11. _____
12. _____
13. _____
14. _____
15. _____
16. _____

# Join Us 1

***Directions***  Write a word from the box after each word below to form a new word.

any _____

grand _____

may _____

can _____

break _____

after _____

in _____

every _____

basket _____

flash _____

| |
|---|
| ball |
| fast |
| thing |
| side |
| light |
| one |
| mother |
| not |
| be |
| noon |

Compound Words

59

*Structural*

# Join Us 2

**Directions**   Write a word from the box after each word below to form a new word.

any _____

my _____

birth _____

pop _____

some _____

with _____

snow _____

out _____

sub _____

rail _____

side

one

out

thing

road

self

way

corn

storm

day

# Begin Again 1

**Directions**   Write a word from the box in front of each word below to form a new word.

| | |
|---|---|
| any | _____ port |
| butter | _____ board |
| card | _____ stairs |
| base | _____ thing |
| every | _____ room |
| air | _____ less |
| down | _____ berry |
| bee | _____ teen |
| four | _____ ball |
| bed | _____ fly |
| care | _____ body |
| blue | _____ hive |

# Begin Again 2

***Directions***  Write a word from the box in front of each word below to form a new word.

any

out

six

high

flash

some

no

neck

them

side

can

bath

_____ way

_____ lace

_____ walk

_____ thing

_____ room

_____ not

_____ doors

_____ selves

_____ how

_____ teen

_____ body

_____ light

Compound Words

62

*Structural*

# Two to One

**Directions**   Write the contraction from the box next to the words it stands for.

| couldn't | she'll | we're | aren't | let's |
|---|---|---|---|---|
| haven't | isn't | wasn't | you'll | I'll |
| it's | we'll | I'm | I've | won't |

I will _____         I am _____

is not _____         we will _____

will not _____       it is _____

have not _____       I have _____

was not _____        you will _____

she will _____       are not _____

we are _____         could not _____

let us _____

# Make Me Shorter

cannot _____         it is _____

could not _____      let us _____

did not _____        was not _____

do not _____         we will _____

have not _____       will not _____

I will _____         you are _____

I am _____           you will _____

is not _____

Contractions

# Count Me In! *1*

**Directions**  Write the one-syllable and two-syllable words from the box on the right list.

| | | | |
|---|---|---|---|
| again | can't | goat | noise |
| aunt | cookie | heard | our |
| bear | doing | looked | story |
| buy | friend | many | they |

## One-Syllable Words

## Two-Syllable Words

# Count Me In! 2

***Directions***  Write the one-syllable and two-syllable words from the box on the right list.

| | | | |
|---|---|---|---|
| any | body | glad | please |
| asked | cry | ground | squirrel |
| bee | does | guess | turtle |
| being | each | Mr. | uncle |

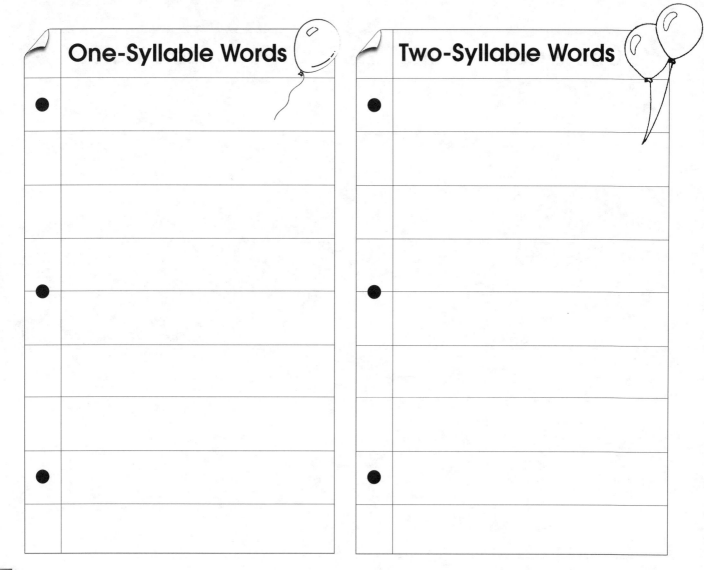

**One-Syllable Words**

- •
- •
- •

**Two-Syllable Words**

- •
- •

Syllables

# One, Two, or Three? *1*

**Directions**   How many syllables does each word in the box have? Write the words under 1, 2, or 3.

| anything | loud | roar | tried |
| I've | might | shovel | twelve |
| join | owl | taken | wasn't |
| library | pennies | telephone | whistle |
| line | piece | thought | won't |
| lion | quiet | tired | yellow |

# One, Two, or Three? 2

***Directions***   How many syllables does each word in the box have? Write the words under 1, 2, or 3.

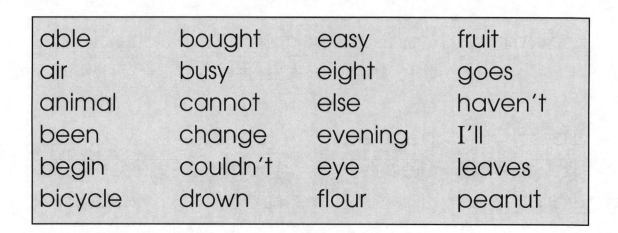

| able | bought | easy | fruit |
| air | busy | eight | goes |
| animal | cannot | else | haven't |
| been | change | evening | I'll |
| begin | couldn't | eye | leaves |
| bicycle | drown | flour | peanut |

**1**                    **2**                    **3**

Syllables

**Directions**   In each blank, write the number of syllables that are in the word.

| | | | | | |
|---|---|---|---|---|---|
| ahead | ___ | orange | ___ | enough | ___ |
| idea | ___ | stories | ___ | bounce | ___ |
| babies | ___ | point | ___ | beauty | ___ |
| afternoon | ___ | television | ___ | continue | ___ |
| anyone | ___ | suddenly | ___ | garage | ___ |
| because | ___ | believe | ___ | curious | ___ |
| board | ___ | elevator | ___ | average | ___ |
| carried | ___ | field | ___ | route | ___ |
| radio | ___ | beautiful | ___ | pour | ___ |
| month | ___ | edge | ___ | power | ___ |
| someone | ___ | feather | ___ | pure | ___ |

Syllables

# Count the Syllables 2

**Directions**    In each blank, write the number of syllables that are in the word.

| | | | | | |
|---|---|---|---|---|---|
| different | ____ | quiet | ____ | hungry | ____ |
| bridge | ____ | swish | ____ | fourth | ____ |
| chimney | ____ | terrible | ____ | already | ____ |
| eight | ____ | elephant | ____ | daughter | ____ |
| Indian | ____ | trouble | ____ | February | ____ |
| minute | ____ | family | ____ | treasure | ____ |
| o'clock | ____ | neighbor | ____ | camera | ____ |
| crawl | ____ | build | ____ | finally | ____ |
| proud | ____ | everything | ____ | ocean | ____ |
| really | ____ | knew | ____ | piano | ____ |
| straight | ____ | clothes | ____ | usual | ____ |

# Match the Words 1

**Directions** First, look at the words under 2. Next, find the same word under 1 or 3. Then draw a line between the same words.

**①**

day

town

log

read

dog

car

tow

play

thank

two

**②**

read

day

can

two

pay

town

red

dig

log

think

**③**

long

can

red

bay

dad

ready

think

pay

down

dig

Word Recognition

Same Word

71

Structural

# Match the Words 2

**Directions**   First, look at the words under 2. Next, find the same word under 1 or 3. Then draw a line between the same words.

### ① 1

our

walk

save

well

take

you

plane

mad

talk

year

### ② 2

well

plane

live

made

year

rake

wall

save

your

take

### ③ 3

plan

safe

made

rake

will

make

live

your

wall

love

# Match the Words 3

**Directions**  First, look at the words under 2. Next, find the same word under 1 or 3. Then draw a line between the same words.

| **1** | **2** | **3** |
|-------|-------|-------|
| but   | want  | ant   |
| went  | smell | too   |
| smell | put   | shell |
| of    | toe   | small |
| want  | off   | when  |
| do    | ant   | put   |
| and   | shall | pet   |
| to    | pet   | shall |
| toe   | do    | pat   |
| hall  | when  | off   |

# Match the Words *4*

**Directions**   First, look at the words under 2. Next, find the
same word under 1 or 3. Then draw a line
between the same words.

| **1** | **2** | **3** |
|-------|-------|-------|
| past  | arm   | blue  |
| ever  | blew  | mall  |
| done  | party | arm   |
| part  | mail  | nice  |
| blew  | ever  | send  |
| nail  | nice  | are   |
| mice  | bone  | party |
| mail  | area  | even  |
| blow  | part  | seed  |
| area  | send  | bone  |

# Color the Word  1

**Directions**   First look for the underlined word in each sentence. Then color the box with the word in it the right color.

Color <u>be</u> red.

Color <u>an</u> blue.

Color <u>box</u> white.

Color <u>by</u> brown.

Color <u>boy</u> green.

Color <u>bee</u> yellow.

Color <u>any</u> black.

Color <u>buy</u> orange.

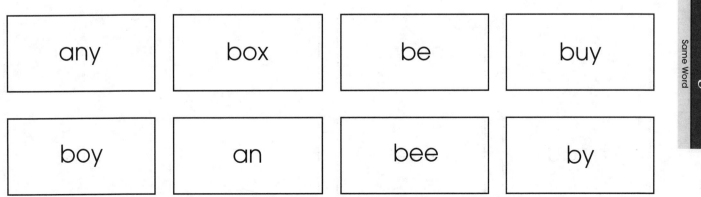

| | | | |
|---|---|---|---|
| any | box | be | buy |
| boy | an | bee | by |

# Color the Word 2

**Directions**   First look for the underlined word in each sentence. Then color the box with the word in it the right color.

Color <u>off</u> red.

Color <u>hear</u> brown.

Color <u>give</u> yellow.

Color <u>head</u> white.

Color <u>five</u> green.

Color <u>gave</u> black.

Color <u>of</u> blue.

Color <u>heard</u> orange.

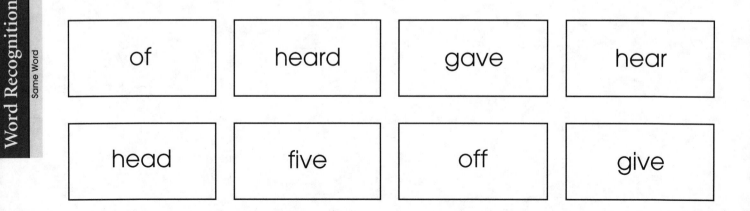

| of | heard | gave | hear |
|---|---|---|---|
| head | five | off | give |

# Color the Word 3

*Directions*  First look for the underlined word in each sentence. Then color the box with the word in it the right color.

Color <u>noise</u> red.

Color <u>Mr.</u> blue.

Color <u>every</u> white.

Color <u>know</u> brown.

Color <u>nose</u> green.

Color <u>ever</u> yellow.

Color <u>Mrs.</u> black.

Color <u>never</u> orange.

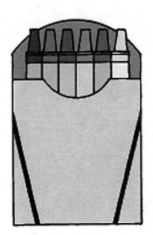

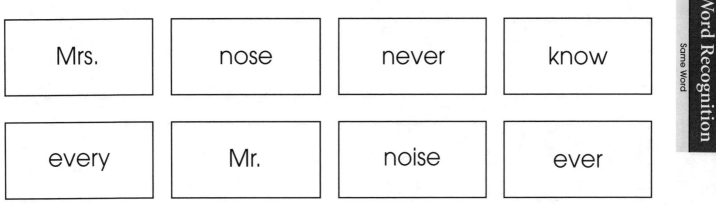

| Mrs. | nose | never | know |
| ---- | ---- | ----- | ---- |
| every | Mr. | noise | ever |

# Color the Word 4

Color <u>each</u> black.

Color <u>then</u> green.

Color <u>call</u> white.

Color <u>for</u> red.

Color <u>them</u> blue.

Color <u>eat</u> brown.

Color <u>four</u> yellow.

Color <u>calf</u> orange.

| | | | |
|---|---|---|---|
| four | them | calf | each |
| then | eat | for | call |

**Directions**   Circle any small word that is hiding in a bigger word. Do not circle "a."

ab(ou)t          lamb           came

again            penny          hold

alone            store          horse

balloon          their          just

basket           told           kitten

bear             white          last

began            know           miss

never            money          monkey

ready            sing           friend

party            before         clown

# Hide and Seek 2

**Directions**    Circle any small word that is hiding in a bigger word. Do not circle "a."

| | | |
|---|---|---|
| m(or)(in)g | behind | puppy |
| must | can't | rain |
| name | find | sang |
| noise | game | street |
| once | grow | water |
| other | hill | where |
| paint | brown | woman |
| peanut | cold | word |
| heard | never | door |
| ground | town | boat |

**Directions**   Circle any small word that is hiding in a bigger word. Do not circle "a."

a(long)

bring

catch

eat

has

many

show

letter

accent

cattle

pony

then

surprise

automobile

battle

nothing

twin

thing

around

bus

coat

farm

gone

hear

rabbit

coral

# Hide and Seek 4

***Directions***   Under each word, write all the smaller words
of two or more letters that are hiding in it.

astonish

    *as, to, on, ton, is*

arrange

already

another

nothing

camera

window

cherry

company

crowd

escape

finally

garage

history

interesting

journey

known

lonely

president

scarce

scatter

shade

swallow

swift

# Hide and Seek 5

afford                dairy                hesitate

attention             deliver              honest

bandage               dragon               mention

bellows               dreadful             million

bracelet              elegant              museum

cabbage               encourage            opinion

carpenter             gallon               permission

chimpanzee            grateful             position

# Hide and Seek 6

| apartment | friend | stairs |
| --- | --- | --- |
| basket | kitchen | strain |
| breakfast | knew | transfer |
| brother | piece | typewriter |
| bulletin | scowl | uniform |
| candle | shallow | vacation |
| drown | spent | vegetable |
| every | stable | volcano |